NOTE TO PARENTS

All children love to learn their favourite nursery rhymes and to be able to recite them to family and friends.

If your child is not yet old enough to read alone let him or her enjoy the delightful illustrations as you read aloud. Point to the words as you say them and talk about the pictures.

By enjoying books at an early age children will begin to develop a love of literature and be more receptive to learning to read 'proper' books later on in life.

Little Boy Blue
and other rhymes

Illustrated by Gill Guile

Copyright © 1990 by World International Publishing Limited.
All rights reserved.
Published in Great Britain by World International Publishing Limited,
An Egmont Company, Egmont House,
P.O. Box 111, Great Ducie Street,
Manchester M60 3BL.
Printed in Italy
ISBN 0 7235 4482 4

A CIP catalogue record for this book is available from the British Library

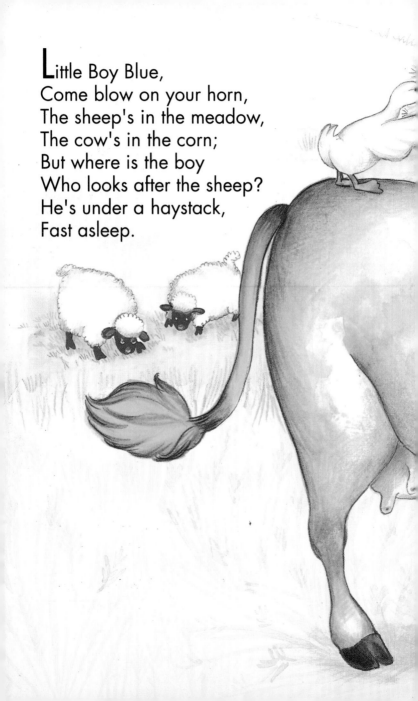

Little Boy Blue,
Come blow on your horn,
The sheep's in the meadow,
The cow's in the corn;
But where is the boy
Who looks after the sheep?
He's under a haystack,
Fast asleep.

Hob, shoe, hob,
Hob, shoe, hob,
Here a nail,
And there a nail,
And that's well shod.

Goosey, goosey gander,
Whither shall I wander?
Upstairs and downstairs
And in my lady's chamber.

If all the world were paper,
And all the sea were ink,
If all the trees were bread and cheese,
What should we have to drink?

Lavender's blue, diddle, diddle,
Lavender's green;
When I am king, diddle, diddle,
You shall be queen.

Call up your men, diddle, diddle,
Set them to work,
Some to the plough, diddle, diddle,
Some to the cart.

Lucy Locket lost her pocket,
Kitty Fisher found it;
There was not a penny in it,
But a ribbon round it.

Hot cross buns!
Hot cross buns!
One a penny, two a penny,
Hot cross buns!

If you have no daughters
Give them to your sons;
One a penny, two a penny,
Hot cross buns!

Cock a doodle doo!
My dame has lost her shoe,
My master's lost his fiddling stick
And doesn't know what to do.

Mary had a little lamb,
Its fleece was white as snow;
And everywhere that Mary went
The lamb was sure to go.

It followed her to school one day,
That was against the rule;
It made the children laugh and play
To see a lamb at school.

Higgledy, Piggledy, my fat hen.
She lays eggs for gentlemen;
Sometimes nine, and sometimes ten,
Higgledy, Piggledy, my fat hen.

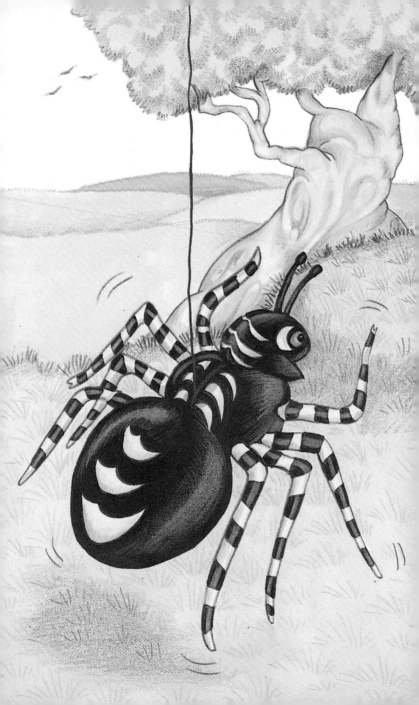

Little Miss Muffet
Sat on a tuffet,
Eating her curds and whey;
Along came a spider,
Who sat down beside her
And frightened Miss Muffet away.

Diddle, diddle, dumpling, my son John,
Went to bed with his trousers on;
One shoe off, and one shoe on,
Diddle, diddle, dumpling, my son John.